SHI

RAINBOW EDITION

The Dog Next Door

and Other Stories

Theodore Clymer

Patricia Miles Martin

Consultants

William E. Blanton

Irene J. Frazier

Milton D. Jacobson

Ken Johnson

Bonnie I. McCullough

Karen A. Scibinico

Roger W. Shuy

E. Paul Torrance

GINN AND COMPANY

Acknowledgments

Grateful acknowledgment is made to the following publishers, authors, and agents for permission to use and adapt copyrighted materials:

Atheneum Publishers, Inc., for the adaptation of the story "Chipmunk Goes Hunting" by Eleanor Clymer. Text copyright © 1965 by Eleanor Clymer. From Chipmunk in the Forest. Used by permission of Atheneum Publishers.

Curtis Brown, Ltd., New York, for the poem "Song of the Train" from Far and Few by David McCord, reprinted by permission of Curtis Brown, Ltd., copyright 1952 by David McCord.

Collins + World Publishing Company for the adaptation of "Here We Go" by Maria Leach. Reprinted by permission of Collins + World Publishing Company from The Thing at the Foot of the Bed and Other Scary Tales by Maria Leach. Copyright © 1959 by Maria Leach.

Gladys Y. Cretan for her story "The Clover Street Trio."

Doubleday & Company, Inc., for the poem "Mice," copyright 1932 by Doubleday & Company, Inc., from Fifty-One New Nursery Rhymes by Rose Fyleman. Reprinted by permission of the publisher.

Berniece Freschet for her stories "The Beavers Build a House" and "Little Pronghorn."

Grosset & Dunlap, Inc., for the poem "Sudden Storm." Reprinted from The Sparrow Bush by Elizabeth Coatsworth. Text Copyright © 1966 by Grosset & Dunlap, Inc. Published by Grosset & Dunlap, Inc.

Harper & Row, Publishers, Inc., for the poem "The Snake" from In the Middle of the Trees by Karla Kuskin. Copyright © 1958 by Karla Kuskin. Reprinted by permission of Harper & Row, Publishers, Inc.

Kathryn D. Henderson for "Down the Mississippi," adapted from Augustus and the River by LeGrand Henderson. Copyright © 1939 by LeGrand Henderson. Copyright renewed. Adapted by permission of McIntosh and Otis, Inc.

J. B. Lippincott Company for "The Mouse Who Liked to Read in Bed." Adaptation of The Mouse Who Liked to Read in Bed by Miriam Clark Potter. Copyright © 1958 by Miriam Clark Potter. Reprinted by permission of J. B. Lippincott Company. Also for the poem "The Goblin." From Picture Rhymes from Foreign Lands by Rose Fyleman. Copyright 1935, renewed 1963 by Rose Fyleman. Reprinted by permission of J. B. Lippincott Company.

Little, Brown and Company for "Fox and the Fire," especially adapted by Miska Miles, with selected illustrations. Text copyright © 1966 by Miska Miles; Illustrations Copyright © 1966 by John Schoenherr. From Fox and the Fire by Miska Miles, by permission of Little, Brown and Co. in association with the Atlantic Monthly Press. Also for the poem "Song of the Train" by David McCord. Copyright 1952 by David McCord. From Far and Few by David McCord, by permission of Little, Brown and Co.

Patricia Miles Martin for the story "No, No, Rosina," adapted from her book No, No, Rosina. Copyright © 1964 by Patricia Miles Martin. Published originally by G. P. Putnam's Sons. Used by permission of the author.

G. P. Putnam's Sons for "The Raccoon and Mrs. McGinnis," adapted from The Raccoon and Mrs. McGinnis by Patricia Miles Martin. Copyright © 1961 by Patricia Miles Martin. Used and adapted by permission of G. P. Putnam's Sons.

The Society of Authors, London, for the poem "Mice" from Fifty-One New Nursery Rhymes by Rose Fyleman. Reprinted by permission of The Society of Authors as the literary representative of the Estate of Rose Fyleman.

The Viking Press, Inc., for the poem "Yucca," from In My Mother's House by Ann Nolan Clark. Copyright 1941, Copyright © renewed 1969 by Ann Nolan Clark. Reprinted by permission of The Viking Press, Inc.

Contents

6

The Dog Next Door

The Bradleys Move In

   William and Lucy Brown sat
on their steps, watching a big van.
   The van was coming along the street.
It stopped at the house next door.
A woman was waiting there in the doorway.
   New people were going to move in. Someone
was coming to live in the house next door.

8

Two movers began to take a big basket
out of the moving van.

"Put that big basket over there, please,"
the woman said. "That's fine."

"I hope a girl moves in there," Lucy said.
Lucy's big cat was sitting on her lap.

William was thinking about the new people.
He hoped there would be a boy in the family.

"I'm going over there and ask if there is a boy
in the family," William said. "You stay here, Lucy."
But Lucy followed him.

The movers were going up the front walk with a big box.

"You can take that box to the back door," the woman said.

The movers took the box. William and Lucy waited by the front door till the woman looked at them and smiled.

"Hello," she said. "Do you live around here?"

"Yes. We live next door," William said.

"I'm Mrs. Bradley. Stanley will be pleased to have you next door."

William was happy.

"There's a BOY in the family," he thought.

10

Mrs. Bradley was still talking.
"Mr. Bradley and Stanley will be coming
very soon."

Along the street came a little car
with a man in it. A great big dog
sat beside him. The car stopped
in front of the house and the dog barked
and jumped out.

WOOF
WOOF

"THAT'S Stanley?" William said.
"Stanley is a DOG?"

Stanley was barking as he came up the walk.
Everyone could see that Stanley was very happy.
And everyone could see that Lucy's cat
and William were not happy at all.

11

The cat jumped down and climbed into an oak tree.
When Stanley barked, the cat climbed higher.

The movers came up the walk
with a big doghouse.

Stanley was still barking,
and the cat climbed still higher.
Up she went—higher—still higher—

"Someone will have to get that cat
down from the tree," Mr. Bradley said.

"The cat will come down," Lucy said.
"She knows about that oak tree."

The movers looked at Mrs. Bradley.
"We are almost finished. Everything is
in the house but this. Where does it go ?"

"Move the doghouse back by the fence, please,"
Mrs. Bradley said.

Stanley followed them around back.
Lucy's cat came down from the oak tree
and ran home.

When the movers came back, Stanley came too,
and jumped up on William.

"Say, Mrs. Bradley," William said.
"Would it be all right if I take Stanley
for a walk ?"

"Stanley would like that very much,"
Mrs. Bradley said.

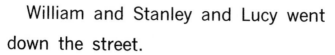

William and Stanley and Lucy went
down the street.

"This is where OUR family lives, Stanley,"
Lucy said. "We live here with our mother
and father. And the cat that climbed
up in your oak tree was MY cat.
You and the cat have to be friends."

"Stanley doesn't know about talk,"
William said.

"How do you know?" Lucy asked.
William didn't know how to answer.
He thought about this for a long time.

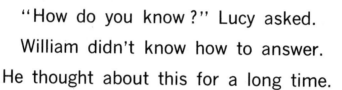

14

Stanley was having a good time.
Every now and then he ran away, looking
in people's gardens. But each time,
he came right back and walked beside William.
William was feeling better now.

"This is a nice dog," William said. "It's
almost as good as having a boy next door."

"It's not almost as good as having a boy
next door," Lucy said. "It's better."

Things I Like

I like a little ladybug
Crawling on my thumb,
I like a little humming-bird,
Hum-hum-hum-

I like a little sea shell,
And dandelion fuzz,
Or a brave little bumble-bee,
Buzz-buzz-buzz-

I like a little lizard
Hiding in the dark,
But most, I like a puppy,
Bark-bark-bark.

Patricia Miles Martin

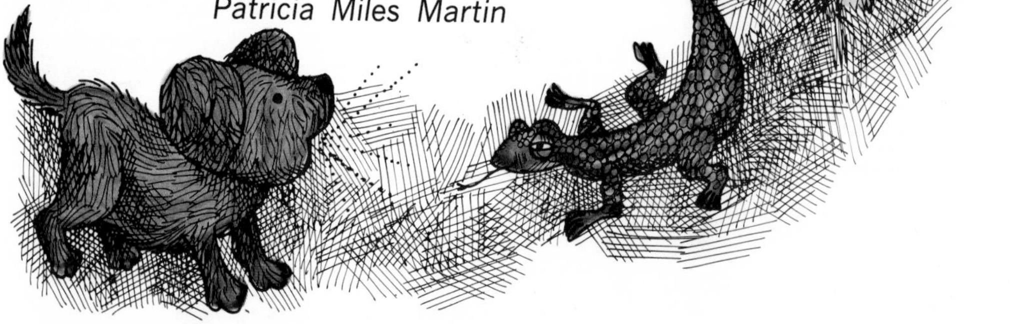

16

It Looks Like Rain

"William," Mrs. Brown said.
"I want you to put your raincoat on
when you go to school today.
It looks like rain."

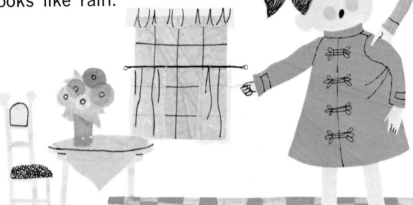

She looked at Lucy. This was Lucy's
first week of school. "And Lucy,
I want you to put your raincoat on too."

"I don't need a raincoat," Lucy said.
"I can take my umbrella."

"Put your raincoat on and take your umbrella
too," their mother said.

William went to get the raincoats
and an umbrella.

Lucy put on her raincoat. She looked
at the umbrella.

"This is the old one," she said.
"It has holes in it and rain comes right through.
I'll get all wet when the rain comes through."

Lucy liked having an umbrella to carry
in the rain, but she didn't want to carry one
with holes that would let the rain through.
She went to find her new one.

18

When William and Lucy opened the front door,
Stanley, the dog next door, was waiting.
He decided that he would walk to school
with William and Lucy.

Stanley jumped around, wanting to carry
something. William decided to let him carry
his book bag.

Stanley went off carrying it proudly.
Proudly, Lucy walked with him,
carrying the new umbrella. She wished
it would rain so she could open it.

When they got to school, Stanley put
the book bag on the steps and went back home.
All through the day, Lucy wished for rain.
When it was time to go home from school,
Miss Little said, "Don't forget to put on
your raincoats, and don't forget to take
your umbrellas. There is a gray cloud
in the sky and it looks like rain."
Outside, Lucy looked up at the sky.
The sky was blue-gray. There was a big gray cloud
up there, but it wasn't raining.

Then Lucy looked down the street
and saw Stanley coming to meet her.

He jumped around, wanting to carry something.

"I don't have a thing that you can carry
but my umbrella," Lucy said.

Stanley was still jumping.

Lucy decided to let him carry
her new umbrella.

"All right, Stanley," she said.
"Stop jumping. Here. Take it."

Proudly, Stanley took the umbrella.

Lucy and Stanley started home.

When they were almost home, it started to rain.

"Let me have my umbrella," Lucy said to Stanley.

Stanley backed away.

Lucy started to take the umbrella from Stanley,
but Stanley tugged at it.

"DROP IT," Lucy said. "DROP IT."

Lucy knew that Stanley was not going to drop it.

Lucy's friends were coming along the street.

They all had their umbrellas open but Lucy.

At last Jane Ann came along.

"You can walk under MY umbrella," she said.
"Two of us can fit under it."

They started down the street. Stanley
trotted along, carrying Lucy's umbrella.

The next morning, Lucy went outside to look
at the sky. There was a gray cloud up there,
a very big gray cloud. She decided
that it looked like rain.

Stanley was waiting on the walk.

"I'll have to take my umbrella to school,"
Lucy said to her mother.

"And don't forget to put your raincoat on,"
her mother said.

"I won't forget." Lucy picked up two umbrellas—
her own new one, and the old one.

"What are you going to do with that old umbrella?"
William asked.

"I have decided to let Stanley have it," she said.
"He can have the old umbrella for his own—
his very own!"

They started down the street.
Proudly, Stanley was carrying his own old umbrella.

When they were almost there, it started to rain.

Lucy opened her own new umbrella.

She listened to the drops of rain
on her umbrella.

She listened to the swish—swish—swish of water
when cars went by.

She listened to friends calling to each other.

It was a fine morning.

She and William hurried on to school.

Sudden Storm

The rain comes in sheets
Sweeping the streets,
Here, here, and here,
Umbrellas appear,
Red, blue, yellow, green,
They tilt and they lean
Like mushrooms, like flowers
That grow when it showers.

Elizabeth Coatsworth

25

William Gets His Hair Cut

William Brown needed to have his hair cut.
"Here is money to get your hair cut,"
his father said. "If you hurry back home, I will
take you and Lucy to the baseball game today."
William decided to hurry.
He wanted to go to the game.

William got on his bicycle and started
down the street to go to the barber shop.
Lucy was calling Stanley, the dog next door,
but Stanley decided to follow William's bicycle.

William parked his bicycle outside
the barber shop. Stanley began to push
into the shop ahead of William.

"You stay outside," William said.

He went inside and sat down to wait.
There were four men ahead of him.

William could see Stanley through the window.
Stanley wanted to find another way
to get inside the barber shop. He went
into the shoe shop next door.

Pretty soon Stanley came rushing out.
A woman was running after him.

She looked in the window of the barber shop
and then opened the door.

"Where did that big dog come from?" she asked.
Everyone looked at William.

"He's not MY dog," William said.

"Well, that dog jumped in my window
and walked all over my shoes," she said.

The woman shut the door with a bang.
William watched through the window.
The woman went back to her shop,
and Stanley lay down on the sidewalk
in front of the barber shop.

28

Three men came to get their hair cut,
but Stanley barked at them.

The barber looked at William. "Boy," he said,
"isn't that your dog?"

William looked at his shoes. "No," he said.
"He just followed me. He lives next door
to my house."

"Well," the barber said. "That dog is keeping
people out of my shop. There are people here
ahead of you, but I'll cut your hair now.
I don't want that dog around here.
Get up in the chair. Hurry."

William got up in the chair, and the barber
moved the chair around and started to work.

29

William's hair fell everywhere.

No one had ever cut William's hair
in such a hurry.

The barber moved the chair around again,
and William got down. He gave the money
to the barber and went outside
and got on his bicycle.

He rode home as fast as he could go,
and Stanley ran ahead of him.

Lucy was on the front steps.
"Dad's waiting for us inside," she said.

His father looked at William's hair.

"It looks fine," he said. "You weren't gone long.
That's what a boy can do when he decides to hurry.
We have a lot of time to get to the ball game."

"He's going some place, so that's why he hurried,"
Lucy said.

"It's the barber who hurried most of all,"
said William.

At the baseball park Lucy sat on one side of her
father, and William sat on the other side.

The wind was cool on the back of William's neck.

William and the Doghouse

William Brown walked into the house
just as his mother picked up the telephone.

"Hello . . . . oh yes, Mrs. Bradley . . . .
Is that so ? . . . . Well, well . . . .
Yes, William will do that for you . . . .
Don't be worried about a thing."

William waited until she set the telephone down.

"What did Mrs. Bradley say ? Why did you say
'don't be worried' ? What do I have to do ?"

32

"The Bradleys are going away for a week or so, and Mrs. Bradley wanted to know if you will take care of their yard and pick up the mail while they are away—"

William waited until she finished talking.

"—And," his mother said, "she wanted to know if you will take care of the dog too."

"I would LIKE to take care of Stanley!" William said. "And I'll take care of their yard and everything too."

William hurried out of the house and ran across his own yard and over to the Bradleys' back door.

Mrs. Bradley showed him what to feed the dog, and then she showed him how to water the grass.

"Don't be worried about a thing," William said. "I'll take care of the yard and of Stanley, too."

"I know you will," Mrs. Bradley said.

"I think I'll take Stanley's doghouse across the yard to OUR house, while you're gone," said William.

Everyone waved good-by when Mr. and Mrs. Bradley went away in their car.

All the girls and boys in the block helped William move the doghouse across the yard.

Stanley went with them.

"This dog knows a lot," William said. "He knows 'want-to-go-for-a-walk' and 'where's-the-cat.'"

At last the doghouse was set in William's yard by the back door.

William knew that everything would be fine.

35

When night came, Stanley sat on the grass looking worried. William showed him the doghouse.

"Don't be worried, Stanley," William said. "It's the same old doghouse. Go on in."

Stanley backed away.

William decided that Stanley didn't know what to do and that he would have to show him. William crawled into the doghouse.

Stanley crawled in too.

But now William couldn't get out.

He pushed at Stanley, but Stanley thought William was playing and Stanley pushed back.

William was worried.

36

William wanted to get outside, but Stanley
was in his way. He called for help.

But no one answered.

It was getting hot in the doghouse,

and William was worried. He didn't know what to do.

He thought he would have to stay there all night.

Then he thought of something.

"Stanley," he said. "Where's the cat?
Where's the cat?"

Stanley got up at once and crawled outside
to look for the cat.

William crawled outside too.

"Come on, Stanley," William said.
"You can sleep on the floor by my bed tonight."
They went into the house. William showed Stanley
where to sleep. "There. Down on the floor,"
William said. "Down, Stanley!"

Stanley went to sleep on the floor
and didn't move until morning.

The next morning, William's friends helped
carry the doghouse across the yard
and back to the Bradleys' yard.

The Bradleys Come Home

It was Saturday, and William
was watering the Bradleys' grass.

"You have all the fun," Lucy said.
"You get to take care of Stanley,
and you get to water the grass too.
And I only get to watch. Let me water."

"All right," William said. "You can
water. But keep the hose still so the water
doesn't flip all over the place."

"All right," said Lucy.
"I'll do exactly as you say."

Lucy was standing with her back
against the oak tree. She took
the hose and held it still
for a long time.

Then she gave it one flip.

"You heard me tell you not to flip
the water around," William said.

"I heard," Lucy said.

"Then stop it. You got water
all over me," William said. "Stop it."

So Lucy gave the hose one
more flip.

William looked at Stanley, who was sleeping under the oak tree.

Lucy took a long time to water the grass. The grass looked nice and green.

Stanley woke up and walked over to William. He pushed against William and then wagged his tail. William gave him a pat, and Stanley's tail wagged faster.

Mr. and Mrs. Bradley would be home any time now. They did not come home that day, but next morning William heard Stanley barking. He heard a car door shut with a bang. Then he heard the other car door. He hurried outside.

Stanley jumped around and wagged his tail.

Mrs. Bradley took a basket into the house.
Mr. Bradley took a box out of the back
of the car.

Mrs. Bradley called to Mr. Bradley,
"Better call William right away!"

"William's here," Mr. Bradley called back.
"Hello there, William. Everything looks fine. Nice work,
William. We knew you would do a good job."

William was very pleased. "I liked doing it,"
he said.

"Mrs. Bradley and I have something for you,
William. It's a surprise. Your mother and father
said you could have it. We thought
you would be pleased. Come on in."

William and Stanley followed Mr. Bradley
into the house.

There in a basket was a little puppy.

"We knew you would like him," Mrs. Bradley said.
"Someday this puppy will look just like Stanley."

At first, William didn't know what to say.
Then he knew.

"It's just exactly what I want," he said.

"We knew you would like him," Mrs. Bradley said.

"There's only one thing better than having
a dog next door," William said, "and that's having
a dog of your very own."

He picked up the puppy. It pushed against
William and licked his chin. And then it wagged
its tail, exactly as Stanley did.

43

What Happens Now?

Vowel Puzzles

Think of one vowel letter which can fit into all the blanks in one sentence. Then read the sentence.

1. Th_s sh_p w_ll take a tr_p.

2. The t_p is n_t in the b_x.

3. D_d c_n n_p on his b_ck.

4. A bird can s_ng and flap its w_ngs.

5. T_d m_t a h_n with a b_ll on her n_ck.

6. A d_ck having f_n in the s_n began

to r_n.

7. A tr_tting horse named D_t st_pped on

the t_p of a hill.

8. D_ck sl_d and h_t h_s sh_n.

9. N_n s_t on t_n s_nd, then r_n b_ck

to the l_nd.

Reviewing the generalization that the vowel sound is usually unglided (short) in words of the CVC, CCVC, and CVCC spelling patterns

45

It Is Time

A Little Patch of Back Yard

Jonathan Mack's father was going to paint the back steps.

"I'll go with you," Jonathan said.

They walked outside, and Jonathan sat down in the back yard.

Ants were marching through the grass
in a long parade. Jonathan lay down
on his stomach to watch.

Pill bugs curled up into little balls,
and beetles crawled under little rocks.

One small brown beetle climbed
up a blade of grass. It fell off
and lay on its back
and kicked its legs in the air.

Jonathan turned it over, and
the beetle hurried away.

Down came a robin. The robin tipped
its head this way and that.

"The robin hears a worm in the ground,"
Jonathan said.

"H'm," said his father.
He stopped to look.
The robin tugged and tugged.

Then—there came Mrs. Fell's cat.

The cat came creeping—creeping—slow—slow.

"Watch that cat!" Jonathan's father said.

"I'll watch," said Jonathan.

"I won't let it get in the paint."

SWISH—

A jay darted down over the cat's head.
The cat jumped back. Away it went—
up and over the fence.

"Cat's gone," Jonathan said.

Away went the robin.
And away went the jay.

The little ants were still marching
in their long parade.

Jonathan's father had been working
a long time. "Well," he said,
"I've finished my paint job."
He sat down beside Jonathan.
"Time to rest," he said.

A beetle lit on Mr. Mack's hand,
and he watched it a while.

"One patch of back yard is like a little world," Jonathan said. "You can see everything here—from an ant parade to a bird digging for its food. Almost everything's looking for something to eat."

He thought of the refrigerator. "I think I'll go inside," he said. "I'll go the front way. I'll be right back."

"H'm," said his father. "Get something for me too."

"Iced tea?" asked Jonathan. "And maybe some chips?"

"That would be good," his father said. "Time for a snack."

I Walk the Long Way

I leave the hogan in the morning.
I walk the long way to the bus stop.
The morning is beautiful.

A quail sits on her nest under the cactus—
small quail-nest under the cactus.
Quietly I walk. Quietly.

56

I wait here at the bus stop.
Blue sky is over me.
Yellow-brown sand is under my feet.
The land is beautiful.
I hear the rattle of the school bus.
The school bus stops for me.

It is time to sit and listen to my teacher.

I learn a new language.

I laugh and my teacher laughs with me.

Now I take the long way back to the hogan.
Quietly, the quail sits
on the nest
under the cactus.
I walk softly.

I am home.
I take a pail of water to the field—
a pail of water for the corn—
a pail of water for the thirsty corn.
The sunset is beautiful.

The moon is high.

It is time to sit and listen to the old ones.

It is time to learn the stories of my people.

The words are beautiful.

A cloud hides the moon.
I hear a coyote calling in the night—
coyote calling in the black night.
The night is beautiful.

A Night in the Mountains

Jennifer West and her mother and father were on their way to stay in the mountains for a night.

"We'll be in camp before lunch time," Jennifer's father said.

"I hope we didn't forget anything," her mother said. "We have coffee, beans, hot dogs, and buns."

"And sleeping bags," said Jennifer. "And nuts for the chipmunks."

They went up steep hills and through
little valleys, and at last—
there they were—under the pine trees,
in a beautiful camp.

"I'll open a can of beans right away,"
said Mrs. West.

"And I'll get out the hot dogs,"
said Mr. West.

Mrs. West looked in the bags and boxes.
"Where is the can opener?"
They all looked for the can opener.

A woman and a girl were sitting by a small tent.

"Hello," Jennifer's mother said. "I'm Kay West. We can't find our can opener. Do you have one we may borrow?"

"I'm Nan Chase," the woman said. "And this is Lisa. We all have to borrow something. We had to borrow a pan. Lisa, please get the can opener."

Soon coffee and beans and hot dogs were
ready, and Jennifer's family and Lisa's
family sat together to eat their lunches.

"I like the smell of the pine trees,"
Mrs. West said.

"I like the smell of coffee on the
campfire," Jennifer said.

After lunch, Jennifer and Lisa went
all around camp. "Look!
Two rabbits!" Jennifer said.
She watched them hop away.

"And a snake!" said Lisa.
The snake slid under a log.

"But where are the chipmunks?"
Jennifer asked.

Almost as if he had heard Jennifer,
a little chipmunk came down from a pine
tree. Jennifer put a nut on the ground
for the chipmunk. "One for you,
and one for me, and one for Lisa,"
Jennifer said. The chipmunk sat up
on his back feet and ate the nut.

While the girls were eating the nuts,
they saw a beautiful black and white animal
slowly making its way along the ground.

"What was that?" asked Lisa.

"I don't know," said Jennifer. "I've
never seen an animal like that before."

Jennifer and Lisa looked all around
camp until time for dinner. When
Jennifer smelled coffee, she knew
it was time to eat. So she and Lisa
hurried back together.

After dinner, all the people in camp sat and
talked and laughed together.

"Tonight I'm going to leave the nuts
by my sleeping bag," Jennifer said.
"Maybe the chipmunk will come
looking for them."

Jennifer got into her sleeping bag
before dark and watched the stars come out
in the sky. And then she went to sleep.

Sometime in the night, Jennifer heard something moving around. She sat up.

In the light of the moon, she saw the beautiful black and white animal again. It was creeping around her father's sleeping bag.

"Daddy," Jennifer said. "What is that animal?"

"Don't move," her mother said. "It's a skunk." Then the skunk went on its way.

"Is it gone?" Jennifer asked.

"I think so," said her mother.

"I HOPE so," said her father. "When I was little, I saw a skunk. It was afraid of me, and that skunk gave off a smell I can still remember."

The next morning, Lisa and Jennifer talked about the skunk.

"It wasn't afraid of us," Jennifer said. "But we were afraid of it."

The little chipmunk came near and sat waiting. Jennifer gave him a nut. "One for you, one for me, and one for Lisa," she said.

It was almost time to start home.
"We have had such a good time together,"
Mrs. Chase said. "Maybe we can all come
back again sometime."

"Did you hear that?" Lisa said.

"I heard!" said Jennifer. "I'll write
to you. Maybe we can come back at
the same time."

"And I'll write to you too," Lisa said.

Then Jennifer and her mother and father
were on their way—back down steep hills
and through the small valleys.
And after a time, they were home.

The next day after school, Jennifer
decided to write to Lisa.

Dear Lisa,

Today, we all had
to talk about a good time
we remember. I talked
about you and the
chipmunk and the skunk.
When we all go back
to the mountains, I hope
our chipmunk will still be
there. But I hope the
skunk goes to another camp.
Write soon.

Love,
Jennifer
XXOOX

The Snake

A snake slipped through the thin green grass
A silver snake
I watched it pass
It moved like a ribbon
Silent as snow.
I think it smiled
As it passed my toe.

Karla Kuskin

76

Rosa and the Crow

From a branch in an oak tree,
a crow looked out over the neighborhood.
Near the tree, Rosa could see
Mr. Cid's back door.

Mr. Cid was at home by himself.
Mrs. Cid and their two children
were away.

"I wonder how he's getting along,"
Rosa thought.

Mr. Cid came out on the back step.
He had a red shirt and a spool of red
thread in his hands. He put them
down on the step.

"Hi, Mr. Cid," Rosa said.
"How are you getting along?"

"Everything's going all right,"
Mr. Cid said.

"I'm going to sit here in the sun
and mend a little rip in this old shirt
before I go to work. It's the only clean
shirt I have left."

The telephone rang. Mr. Cid ran
into the house to answer it.

Rosa heard a noise in the oak tree.

CAW—CAW—CAW

She looked up. The crow sat
on a low branch in the tree.
Then down it came with a swish.
And there it was—a beautiful crow
on Mr. Cid's step.

The crow picked up the spool of red
thread, and with a swish it was gone—
back to its branch in the tree.
Rosa watched. A bit of bark was
loose on the tree, and the crow
poked the thread under the bark.

Mr. Cid came outside.
"That was my wife," he said.
"She and the boys will be home tonight.
And NOW—I have to get busy.
It's almost time for work."

He sat down on the step
and picked up the shirt.
"Where's the thread?" he asked.
He looked on the step.

"Mr. Cid. . . ." Rosa said.

"I'm sorry. I don't have time to listen," Mr. Cid said. "I have to find that spool of thread."

"But Mr. Cid. . . ."

"It's almost time for your bus, Rosa," Mr. Cid said. "Why don't we talk when we both have more time?"

82

Rosa looked up at the oak tree.
There was the spool of thread—
a small red dot in the green
oak tree. Mr. Cid was right.
It WAS almost time for the school bus.
So Rosa went down the street to wait for it.
She wondered what Mr. Cid would do.

Up in the oak tree, the crow sat
on a high branch and looked
out over the neighborhood.
CAW—CAW—CAW—

Workers and Tools

Match the workers with the tools they use in their work.

Draw pictures of tools these workers would use.

WET PAINT

Which?

Look at the pictures. Can you answer the questions below?

Which one or ones

could become a farmer?   will grow taller?

is a learner?   is bigger than the others?

is a climber?   will never be smaller?

might become a batter?   grows higher each year?

could be a swimmer?   is greener in summer?

will be a runner?   will not grow younger?

Make up questions of your own, using words that end in *er*.

Wild Creatures

How the Bear Got His Supper

There was no noise in the forest.
Rabbits hopped on soft little rabbit feet
in the wild grass, looking for their supper.
Chipmunks ran on soft little chipmunk feet
and ate their supper up in an old oak tree.
A little mouse came creeping . . . creeping . . .
There was no noise in the forest—
only the birds sang
in the top of the old tree.

And then, CRASH-BANG,
a bear—a big black bear—
came into the forest.
    The rabbits didn't move.
    The chipmunks were still.
    The mouse ran under a log.
    The birds called softly,
"Cheep . . . . cheep . . . ."

The bear stopped under the oak tree.

He was a hungry bear—a very hungry bear.

He looked up into the tree.

There in the oak tree was his supper—
a supper of fat acorns. But the acorns
were high—high up in the tree.

The hungry bear could not reach them.

But he knew how he would get his supper.

He climbed into the tree.

Up, up he climbed. But he did not reach
for the acorns.

He crawled out on a big branch of the tree.
He sat there and then he rocked the branch.
Up and down. Up and down.

And the branch broke with a CRASH-BANG.

Down they fell, branch and acorns
and big black bear. CRASH-BANG.

The bear rolled over. He sat up
and looked around. With his big, big paws,
he reached for the acorns.

He reached for more, and he ate his fill.

And while he ate his supper, the rabbits
and the chipmunks were still.
And only the birds called,
"Cheep . . . . cheep . . . ."

And when he was not hungry, the bear
went out of the forest with a crash and a bang.
CRASH-BANG.

And when he was gone, the rabbits looked
for their supper.

Chipmunks ran high up into the tree
and down again and hid acorns in the brush.

The little mouse came creeping . . . creeping . . .

Again there was no noise in the forest—
only the birds sang in the old oak tree.

Wild Things

On the side of a hill a little pack rat
is hunting for her supper. The pack rat
is hungry. And while she hunts, she is afraid—
very afraid—for the pack rat has many enemies.

And some of the pack rat's enemies are these:
Owl and Eagle, Fox and Bobcat, and

SNAKE.

Crawling—crawling, the snake is hunting
for his supper. He, too, is hungry.
And while he hunts, he is afraid, for the snake
has many enemies. And some of his enemies
are these: Owl and Eagle, Bobcat and

FOX.

The old fox barks at the moon. She is hungry.
She starts out to hunt for her supper.

She prowls over the hill and down again.

She prowls through the brush, and she is afraid.

When the fox was very little, she was afraid
of Owl and Eagle.

Now that she is old, she is afraid of

BOBCAT.

The bobcat prowls through the forest.
He prowls through the green forest
on big, soft feet. He makes no noise.
He is very hungry and he is afraid.
He is afraid of

PEOPLE.

Little Pronghorn

Alone, a little pronghorn lay waiting in the brush.

Far away, its mother ran across the open country.
A coyote was running after her. She led
the coyote far from the place where the
little pronghorn lay.

The coyote would not catch her for she
ran very fast—and no coyote could run
as fast as the mother pronghorn could run.

The little pronghorn lay very still.

Late that day a girl and her father
started for a ride. The girl saw the little pronghorn
in the brush. They stopped their horses.

"Where can its mother be?" the girl asked.

"I don't know," her father said, "but the
mother will not stay away long.
She will be back soon."

Then they heard the bark of a coyote
from far away. They heard the coyote bark again.

"The coyote is coming this way," the girl said.

"That coyote is prowling around looking for food.
He would like to find this little pronghorn here," her
father said. "We'll have to take the pronghorn with us."

The little pronghorn lay very still. The girl picked
it up and took it home in her arms. The little
pronghorn was only one day old, and it was
very small.

At home the girl gave the little pronghorn some milk. It was very hungry.

Little Pronghorn was beautiful. It had a red-brown coat. It had some white hair on its face and around its tail and some on its stomach. Its legs were very long.

"When Little Pronghorn stands up, its legs look like sticks," the girl said. "How can it ever learn to run on those funny little stick legs!"

"It won't take Little Pronghorn long to learn," her father said. "It will learn by the time it's about three days old, and soon it will run faster than the coyote. Pronghorns can run faster than all other animals in the land."

On the open grassland, when a pronghorn lies flat against the ground, it looks like the ground where it lies. Very soon it learns to lie flat against the ground. If a pronghorn lies very still without moving, and if it lies very flat, its enemies will not see it.

But sometimes it is afraid.

Around the pronghorn's tail is a ring of white hair. When a pronghorn is afraid, the white hair on its tail stands up in the ring. The ring of hair can be seen from far away, flashing white in the light of the sun.

It tells other pronghorns to watch for their enemies—to watch for coyote or eagle, prowling bobcat or mountain lion.

When a pronghorn is about three days old,
it can run and play.

So, very soon, when the girl raced her horse
down the road, Little Pronghorn raced with her.
It seemed to fly.

The day came when it was time
for Little Pronghorn to go back to the herd.

"A pronghorn is wild," the girl said.
"It must go back to the others
and live with the herd."

One morning when she rode her horse,
and Little Pronghorn raced with her,
she saw a herd of pronghorns.

The herd was standing on a far hill.

The little pronghorn knew the herd was there.
Its mother was with them.

Little Pronghorn ran fast, away
across the flat land and up the hill. The girl
watched it go. The pronghorn ran faster
than it had ever run before.

Little Pronghorn did not look back.
On it went—on and on, until it
was safe with the herd on the hill.

THE BEAVERS BUILD A HOUSE

The sun goes down and night will come soon.

Wild animals come softly from the woods.

They come to the pond to drink.

Two beavers swim across the pond.

It is time for them to go to work.

Beside the water are many young trees.
The beavers climb out of the water.
Each picks a young tree. And each stands
on its back legs and leans on its wide, flat tail.

They chew the bark of the young trees.
As they chew, chips fall to the ground.
The beavers chew almost through the trees.

A tree leans.

It leans a little more—

WHACK!

A beaver's tail hits the ground.

This is the beaver's way of saying DANGER.
One of the young trees is about to fall,
and the beavers hurry away from the falling tree.
They hurry to the pond and dive deep down
into the water away from danger.

The tree falls to the ground.
It falls with a great CRASH!

After a while the beavers come to the tree
where it lies on the ground. They chew off
the branches. Now they stop chewing and listen
for danger. They listen for the coyote
and the bobcat.

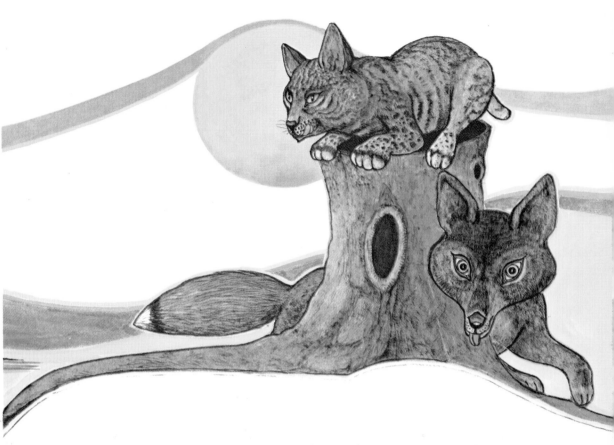

The beavers take the branches
from the young tree to make a house.
They carry the branches out into the water
and put them in the mud down deep in the pond.
Again and again they carry branches.
In the pond, they make a pile of branches
that is higher than the water. The pile
of branches can be seen above the water.
This is the floor of their house.

They work many nights building this house.

They carry armloads of mud—
then more and more armloads.

They put mud on the floor of branches.
They make a mud pile two feet high, on top
of the branches. Then they put sticks and
more mud on top of it all.

They dive deep under the water, and they dig
two tunnels. These two tunnels go through
the great pile of mud and branches
to the place where their house will be.

They start to dig a cave in the mud.
When they dig the cave, they carry
armloads of mud out through their tunnels.

At last they have a house to live in.
They leave one little hole in the top
of the house for air to come through.

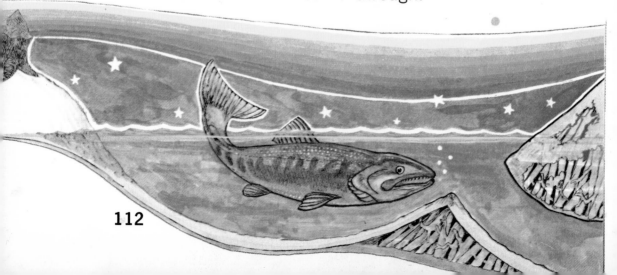

One side of the house is high,
and the other is low.

Their house is ready.

The beavers store food to last
all the winter long. Out through tunnels
they go for food. In through tunnels
they carry armloads of branches.

They take the branches to the low side
of the house.

Here on the low side they will eat.

They will sleep and rest on the high
side.

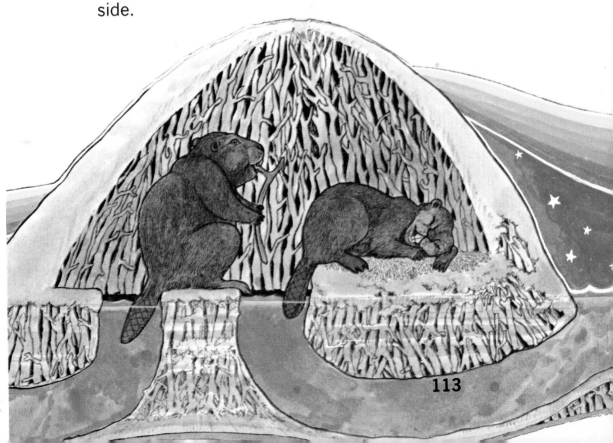

The nights are long, and snow falls.

Outside, far away, the bark of a hungry coyote is heard.

But in the beaver house two beavers are safe; safe from the coyote, safe from the bobcat, safe from all danger.

The Sea Otter

The sun comes up. A hungry otter
dives deep into the sea to look for her food.
Down she goes—down—
down.

She catches a fish and swims up with it.

Up—up through the water.

The otter floats on her back.

And she eats her fill.

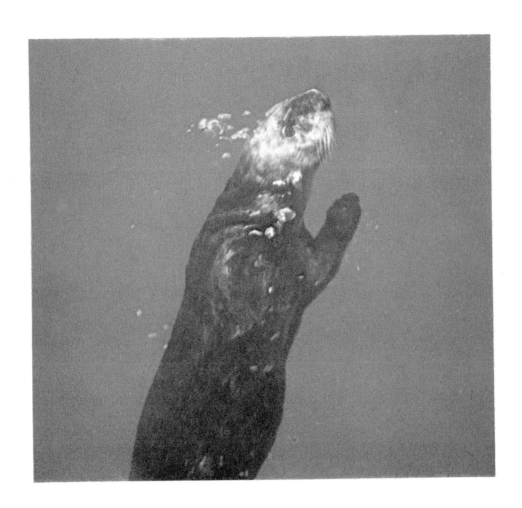

The otter dives again, but this time she
is not looking for food.
She wants to find something to play with.
She finds a little rock, and she swims
up through the sea again.

Up—up through the green water.

She flips the rock into the air and she catches it. And if she drops it, down she goes after it, and she finds it and comes up again. The game goes on and on. And when at last, she is through with the rock, she lets it fall into the sea. And she plays with the otters in the herd.

They jump up from the water, high into the air. They flip over and over.
They jump again.

All day long, the otter plays and looks for food and plays again. Now she dives deep and she finds a clam.

The otter swims up with the clam
in one front paw, and a rock in the
other paw.

She floats on her back, and she puts
the rock on her stomach.

She hits the clam against the rock, and she eats bits of good food. A bit of clam shell falls on her stomach. And the otter flips over and over, and washes her stomach in the sea.

Night comes, and the sea otter swims
to a bed of seaweed.
She pulls the seaweed around her.

She floats there on her back,
with seaweed for her bed.
She rocks with the tide, and she sleeps.

Animal Babies

Have you ever seen a baby animal just after it was born? Read about three kinds of newly born animal babies.

Black bear mothers have from one to four babies at a time. The babies are very small. New baby bears cannot see. They have no fur.

Baby chipmunks are born without fur. Their eyes are closed at first. There may be four or five in a family.

New baby rabbits have no fur and they are blind for a while. There may be from four to seven in a litter.

Ask your teacher to make a chart like the one on the next page. Then fill in the chart from the facts that you have just read.

Making a chart of story details

	bears	chipmunks	rabbits
How many babies are born?			
Can the babies see when they are born?			
Are the babies covered with fur?			

Look at your chart when you have filled it in.
From the facts on the chart, which sentences
below could you say are true?

Rabbit, chipmunk and bear babies:

1. are born blind.

2. can run around right away after they are born.

3. are quite helpless at first.

4. have no fur at first.

5. play with each other right away.

6. are born without fur.

7. have brothers and sisters born at the same time.

126

Clickety-Clack

127

Song of the Train

Clickety-clack,
Wheels on the track,
This is the way
They begin the attack:
Click-ety-clack,
Click-ety-clack,
Click-ety, *clack*-ety,
Click-ety
Clack.

Clickety-clack,
Over the crack,
Faster and faster
The song of the track:
Clickety-clack,
Clickety-clack,
Clickety, clackety,
Clackety
Clack.

Riding in front,
Riding in back,
Everyone hears
The song of the track:
Clickety-clack,
Clickety-clack,
Clickety, *clickety*,
Clackety
Clack.

David McCord

Carmelita's Birthday

Carmelita knew exactly what she wanted for her birthday. Exactly. "Daddy," she said, "I know what I want for my birthday."

"And what is that?" asked her father.

"I'd like to have our family go somewhere together," she said.

"Where?" asked her brother, Ricardo.

"How about the aquarium?" Carmelita asked. "Remember when Grandma came to visit us and took us to the aquarium? I miss Grandma. Grandma always laughed a lot, and when Grandma laughed, I laughed too."

"I think it would be fine to go somewhere on your birthday," their father said. "Make up your mind where you want to go, Carmelita."

Carmelita thought about it. "I wouldn't mind going to the aquarium again," she said.

"Maybe a new place would be better," Ricardo said.

"Maybe," Carmelita said. She thought again. "I think I'd like to go to the airport," she said to her father.

"That's a great idea," said their father. "We'd all like that."

At last it was the morning of Carmelita's birthday. All of her family went to the airport. Carmelita watched the people who were waiting for planes. They were walking back and forth—back and forth.

A voice boomed out. The voice was telling about planes that were going and planes that were coming, but no one seemed to listen.

There were machines for everything. Carmelita had popcorn out of one machine, and Ricardo had peanuts out of another. Her mother and father had coffee out of a coffee machine. There were more machines than Carmelita had ever seen in one place before.

Carmelita watched people who were getting off a plane. "There's GRANDMA!" she said.

"SURPRISE," said Ricardo. "We knew that Grandma was coming for a visit. It was a surprise for your birthday. But you picked the right place to go."

"I've got a secret," Carmelita said.

"What's the secret?" Ricardo asked.

"I was REALLY wishing to see Grandma too!" Carmelita said.

135

"Carmelita!" Grandma gave her a hug. "I couldn't stay away on your birthday. I had to get here in time to see you blow out the candles on your birthday cake."

"When I get ready to blow out the candles," Carmelita said, "I won't even have to make a wish!"

Grandma laughed. And Carmelita laughed too.

Lost and Found Department

William and his mother and father and their dog, Chips, lived on the first floor of an old brownstone house. They had lived there as long as William could remember. He liked the old house with big fireplaces to keep them warm.

And now the last of the brownstone houses in the block would be torn down, and there would be a big apartment house where the old brownstones had been.

Down the street was a big apartment house, where many of William's friends lived. "If we have to move, I'd like to live there," William said.

"I'd like to live there too," his mother said.

William's mother and father went down the street to talk to Mrs. Green about an apartment in her big apartment house.

"I'm sorry that your brownstone house is going to be torn down, and I would like to have your family," Mrs. Green said. "But you have that big dog. I don't want dogs in my apartment house."

After lunch William sat down to think. He was sorry that his own old brownstone house had to be torn down.

Fred Barber rode by on his bicycle. Fred lived in Mrs. Green's apartments, and William wished he could live there too. But he had to live where his dog could live.

Chips trotted off down the street.

Chips was a good dog. He didn't bark much, and he picked up all the litter that he found in the street. He picked up more than litter. He picked up everything he found in people's yards too!

William whistled for Chips.

Chips came trotting up, carrying a torn coat. He gave it to William.

"Thank you," William said. "This doesn't look exactly like litter." He looked at the coat. It belonged to Fred Barber. Fred had left it outside somewhere.

William went to Fred's apartment house and gave the coat to Fred.

He stopped and looked up at the apartment house. Then he thought to himself, "Chips and I make a good team. We are like a Lost and Found Department." He decided to talk to Mrs. Green.

Then he rang Mrs. Green's bell.

"Mrs. Green," he said. "I know you don't want dogs in your apartment house, but I'd like to live here. My dog would like it too. He knows this neighborhood."

"No," Mrs. Green said, "I don't want dogs in my apartment house."

"He is a GOOD dog," William said. "He doesn't bark much. He picks up all the litter he finds in the street. Your yard would always be clean. Chips would pick up every bit of torn paper—every bit of litter.

"He picks up things that are lost too. When he finds something, he comes carrying it to me, and I take it back where it belongs. We could be your Lost and Found Department."

Mrs. Green smiled. "So far, William, we get along very well without a Lost and Found Department."

William was not happy. He started home to his old brownstone house.

Chips trotted off by himself. After a while he came back with a toy bear. He gave the toy bear to William. William took it back to Jill Gray, and came home and sat on the steps of his old brownstone house.

When Chips came home again, he walked proudly, carrying a handbag. He gave it to William.

"Thank you," William said. He hurried inside his house. "Look what Chips found," he said to his mother. "It has money in it. It rattles!"

"Open it and see if there is a name inside," she said.

William opened the handbag.

"There is a lot of money here," he said. He looked and found a paper with a name on it. "It's Mrs. Green's!" he said.

William and Chips ran all the way to the apartment house.

Mrs. Green was standing on the front walk, talking to Mrs. Barber. "I don't know WHERE I could have left it," she said. "I was on my way downtown with the rent money, when I saw that my handbag was gone."

"Here it is!" William called.

"William," Mrs. Green said. "WHERE did you find it?"

"I didn't find it," William said. "My DOG found it!"

"Well," Mrs. Green said. "Well." She opened the handbag. "Everything is here." She looked at Mrs. Barber. "Mrs. Barber, I don't think the people in our apartment house would mind having ONE dog living here, do you?"

"I'd like to have a dog like Chips," Mrs. Barber said.

"William," Mrs. Green said. "Go home and tell your mother that I'd like to have your family here." She shut her handbag with a click. She patted Chips. "It will be a very good thing to have a dog here. I think that every apartment house needs a good Lost and Found Department," she said.

144

Red Tulips

Henry lived on the first floor of Mr. and Mrs. Camp's apartment house.

In front of the apartment house was a small garden.

In this garden Mrs. Camp had planted red tulip bulbs.

The tulip bulbs bloomed in the springtime.

Each springtime there were more and more tulips.

One fall when the tulips had stopped blooming, and their leaves were brown, Mrs. Camp said, "The tulip bulbs have multiplied. There are too many of them. I will take some of them out."

So Henry and Mrs. Camp dug up the tulip bed and raked it fine with a rake.

When they had planted the bulbs, many of them were left over.

"Now what shall I do with the tulip bulbs?" Mrs. Camp said.

"I would like to ask my friends if they want them," Henry said.

"Good," said Mrs. Camp. "Go and ask your friends."

Henry put the bulbs in a big basket.

He looked up at the apartment building.

On the second floor there were many window boxes.

Henry went up the steps and knocked at every door.

Everyone on the second floor was glad to have tulip bulbs for their window boxes.

On the next floor he knocked on Mr. Black's door.

"Would you like to have some tulip bulbs?" Henry asked.

And Mr. Black, who had no window box, said, "I'd be glad to have some tulip bulbs. Tulips always tell me that spring has come. I'll put them in pots and set them on my window sill."

When Henry got to the very top floor, he had only one tulip bulb left. On this top floor, Mrs. May lived alone.

"Would you like a tulip bulb?" Henry asked. "I'm sorry I have only one left."

"I don't have a thing to plant it in," Mrs. May said. "But I'm glad to have one bulb. I will FIND something to plant it in."

So all the people in the apartment house planted tulips that day.

Winter passed and then spring came.

With water and with sun, the bulbs grew in the little garden outside the apartment house.

With water and with sun, they grew in window boxes. They grew in brown pots.

First there were wide leaves, and then came the tulips.

In all the windows in that apartment house red tulips bloomed.

They bloomed in window boxes and in brown pots.

And on the very top floor in Mrs. May's apartment, one beautiful red tulip bloomed in a blue teapot.

All the neighbors saw the red tulips blooming there, and they knew that Henry was everyone's friend.

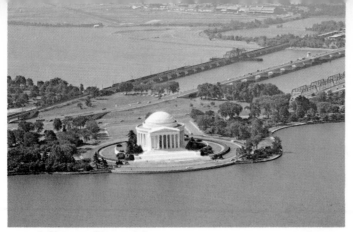

Jefferson Memorial

White House

Lincoln Memorial

150

The United States Capitol Building and the Surrounding Area

A Great City

When our country was young, the city of Washington, D.C. was built. The city called Washington, D.C. was built in a forest.

It was built near two beautiful rivers.

Wild geese winged their way across the sky, and frogs called from the rivers.

Trees were cut down and the great capitol building was built. Our laws were made in the capitol building.

A house was built. The President of the United States would live in this house.

At that time there was a park near the President's house. And people let their horses and cows, sheep and pigs graze in the park.

Today in that same park there are no horses or cows, sheep or pigs. It is a beautiful park for all people to see.

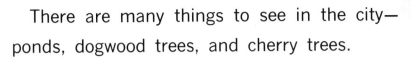

There are many things to see in the city—ponds, dogwood trees, and cherry trees.

This is a city of many monuments.

The highest of all is the George Washington Monument. This monument helps all of us remember George Washington, the first President of the United States.

Inside this monument is an elevator.

Boys and girls from all over the country ride in the elevator to the top.

Inside the monument are many steps. If boys and girls do not want to ride in the elevator, they may climb these steps that wind up and up.

When they reach the top, they see the United States Capitol building with its white dome.

They see many monuments.

They see far off over the winding rivers. They see Arlington Cemetery where lie those who died for our country.

The boys and girls look over this beautiful city—this great city, Washington, D.C.—the capital of our country.

156

The Clover Street Trio

Jen and Linda and Kate lived on Clover Street. They were always together. Because they were three, everyone called them the Clover Street Trio.

They always walked to school together, and they came home together.

Then Jen would hurry out of her flat. Linda and Kate would hurry out of their apartment houses.

Some days one of the girls had three apples. Some days one would have three doughnuts. They were best friends and they liked Clover Street.

Some days they hunted in the clover that grew along the street.

"My grandmother says that if you find a four-leaf clover, you will have good luck," Jen said.

"We don't need a four-leaf clover," Kate said, "because we have good luck now. We live on Clover Street."

"If we want to skate, our sidewalk is just right," Jen said.

"And we always want to skate," said Linda.

"It's good for jump-rope too," Kate said. Two held the rope and one jumped.

One morning there was a new girl in school.

Mrs. Lipman said, "This is Trudy. I hope everyone will be kind to Trudy."

"I'll show her where to put her coat," Johnny said.

"I'll show her where we keep our lunches," said Bob.

After school the Clover Street Trio sat on Jen's front steps, and they had a surprise.

The door of the apartment house across the street opened, and out came Trudy.

"Look," said Jen. "It's the new girl, Trudy."

"I guess she moved into the apartment," Kate said. "Do we want to ask her to play?"

No one answered.

"We can think about it after a while," Linda said.

"Let's skate," said Jen.

The Clover Street Trio skated up and down the block. They did not look at Trudy.

Trudy watched.

Jen and Linda and Kate jumped rope until Trudy went into her apartment house.

After Trudy went inside her apartment house, the Clover Street Trio sat on Linda's steps.

Linda sat with her chin in her hands. "I wonder how it would be if you and Trudy were the Clover Street Trio. I wonder how it would be if I watched," she said.

"I wonder," said Kate.

"Would we have more fun if we asked Trudy to play?" Jen asked.

"Maybe four would be better than three," Kate said.

The next morning Kate and Jen and Linda were waiting when Trudy and her mother came down their steps.

"Trudy can walk with us," Jen said.

"We will take her to school," said Kate.

"Thank you!" Trudy's mother said. She waved good-by to Trudy.

The four girls walked to school together.

"Do you have skates?" Linda asked.
Trudy nodded.

"Do you like to jump rope?" Kate asked.
Trudy nodded again.

"What do you have in your lunch bag?"
Jen asked.

"Cake for one thing," Trudy said.

"Trade you for an apple," said Jen.

When they reached the schoolyard, they all went inside together.

"Here comes the Clover Street Trio," Bob said.

"There can't be a trio with four people," said Johnny.

"We have a new name now," Kate said. "WE'RE the Four-Leaf Clovers."

One Will Do

Read the two sentences in each set. Then think of one word which fits both meanings.

1. If you ride in an airplane you do this.

   This is an insect which people do not like.

2. Most people do this to raw meat.

   This is someone who wears a tall white hat and an apron.

3. When you do this, you lie down and turn over and over.

   This is the name of something you can eat for dinner.

One word will do for two of the pictures. Can you find the pictures that match?

Extending word meanings by finding words that fit two different meanings

What Is in the Block?

Read all the words around the block.
Then read the sentence in the block.
Think of a word that is like the other
words and fits the sentence. What is it?

best

west | You do this after you've worked hard. | nest

test

lack

sack | Your foot makes one in the snow. | pack

crack

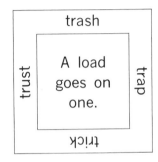

trash

trust | A load goes on one. | trap

trick

flake

flock | It comes from a fire. | flit

flash

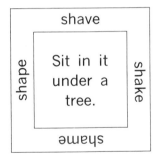

shave

shape | Sit in it under a tree. | shake

shame

still

stiff | You need it to mail a letter. | stump

stuff

skill

skin | You can do this on ice. | skim

skiff

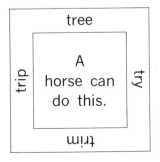

tree

trip | A horse can do this. | try

trim

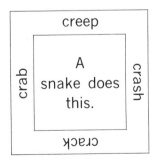

creep

crab | A snake does this. | crash

crack

A Question-
A Question

DOWN THE MISSISSIPPI

Augustus was asleep in the houseboat where he lived with his sister Gloriana, his little brother Jupiter, Pop, Mom, Tom Cat, and the chickens.

They were going down the Mississippi River in a houseboat.

This night they had been asleep for some time when the houseboat tossed around so much that Augustus woke up.

Augustus opened the door and he looked outside.

A big wave washed up.

Gloriana woke up too. "What was that?" she asked.

"We're drifting!" Augustus said. "We're drifting down the old Mississippi!"

The noise of the wind and rain was great.

"What will we do?" Gloriana asked.

"Maybe we can pole to land," Augustus said. "Hand me that pole. No—it won't work. The water's too deep. Listen. I'll sit up and see what I can see. You and Jupiter go back to bed. I'll take the first lookout, and you can take the second one."

"I don't want to go to bed," Jupiter said.

Then they heard a strange noise.

There was a sad sound, high above the wind. It was like something lost and afraid—

The sound came again.

It came from the back door.

"You better lock the door," Augustus said.

"YOU lock it," said Gloriana.

Augustus was afraid to move. Something was pushing against the door. Something wanted to get in.

Jupiter crawled under his bed.

Gloriana jumped into her bed and slid under the sheet.

The sound came again, and the door opened.

Augustus was afraid to look. Something was pushing against his back.

He grabbed it. It was a chair.

A big, shivering, wet, yellow hound dog was standing there. "Woof!" The hound wagged his tail. He crossed the cabin to the stove. The dog lay down in a wet heap, flopped his tail three times against the cabin floor and fell asleep.

Jupiter crawled out from under the bed.

Gloriana still had her head under the sheet.

"Come out," said Jupiter. "It's only a dog."

Augustus went to the door and looked out. A pile of wood drifted against the back deck.

"I guess there was a big flood," Augustus said. "That hound dog must have drifted down river on that pile of wood."

Tom Cat woke up and sniffed at the hound, and then curled up beside him and went to sleep.

The houseboat still drifted on down the Mississippi.

There was no wind.

And the great river rolled along, still and black. A star came out in the sky.

Augustus opened the cabin door and looked outside. The river didn't look so strange, now that the rain and the wind had stopped.

The houseboat seemed big and safe.

Jupiter was asleep.

"I'll keep watch," Augustus said. "I'll take that first lookout."

Gloriana nodded.

"No need to stand up," said Augustus, and he sat down on his bed where he could look through the cabin window.

The houseboat rocked through the night.

Cat and the hound dog were sound asleep.

On one side of the cabin Jupiter and Gloriana were sleeping too.

On the other side Augustus was keeping lookout—FAST asleep.

YUCCA

Yucca
Growing
So tall,
Like candles;
Like candles;
So white,
With a flower
For light.

We twist your little leaves
Into strings of thread;
We knot your strong stems
Into rope.
We weave your fibers
Into mats and baskets;
We pound your roots
For soap to make us clean.

Yucca,
Tall, white Yucca,
You make my heart sing
With your beauty.

Ann Nolan Clark

Chipmunk Goes Hunting

Long ago in the middle of a deep, dark forest, there lived a Chippewa Indian boy. His name was Chipmunk.

Chipmunk lived with his father and mother and his little brother in a house made of logs and bark, near a big lake.

One morning he jumped out of his bed of
furs and ran to the doorway to look out.

His mother was cooking breakfast over a
fire outside the door. She smiled at him.

Today Chipmunk was going hunting with
his Uncle, Many-Deer.

Many-Deer was a chief of the village and a
great hunter. It was an uncle's job to teach
his sister's sons to hunt. And now Chipmunk
was old enough to go with him—old enough
to learn to track animals and to find his way
in the deep woods—to learn to be a hunter.

Chipmunk's father was a great hunter too. He had made the small bow and arrows and the knife with its flint blade—the knife that Chipmunk would take with him into the woods.

Chipmunk knew he must learn to hunt. All the boys were glad when they were big enough to hunt.

One of his friends ran past on the way to the lake.

"You're going out with your uncle today," he called. "You are lucky."

Chipmunk didn't feel lucky. For he had a secret. He was afraid—afraid of the forest.

He knew the paths near his village. He had often gone with the other boys a little way into the forest to hunt rabbits. But he was afraid in the deep woods. It was so still.

Two or three times he had been sent into the woods at night to bring back water from the brook. That was to make a boy brave. But it hadn't made Chipmunk brave. Every leaf that moved and every branch that cracked made him afraid.

He didn't want his uncle to know about this. So Chipmunk kept his secret to himself.

Now he ate the breakfast that his mother gave him.

Soon he saw his uncle coming across the village from his own house.

"Are you ready?" Many-Deer asked.

"I am ready," said Chipmunk, but he did not feel at all ready. And he was a little afraid of his uncle too. Many-Deer was so big, and he didn't smile.

They started out through the trees
following a path that had been made by the
feet of the hunters. Many-Deer went first,
and then Chipmunk followed along.

It was still in the forest. He only heard the
wind in the treetops, the call of the birds,
and the bubbling of a brook.

"This brook runs into our lake,"
Many-Deer said. "It can help you find your
way if you are lost."

"Yes, Uncle," said Chipmunk.

"See the knife marks on the trees beside the trail," said Many-Deer. "If you see these marks, you will know that one of our hunters made them. They will help you find your way, and you can make your own marks with your knife."

"Yes, Uncle," said Chipmunk again.

They walked on along the trail, away from the village, until they were in the deep woods, and Chipmunk hurried to keep up with his uncle.

At last they came to a place in the forest where the sunlight came through the trees.

"This is a good place to watch for deer," said Many-Deer. "They come here often. You stand in back of this tree, and I will go a little way off. Keep very still."

Many-Deer moved away. His feet made no noise on the soft ground. Soon he was gone.

Chipmunk could not see him.

Chipmunk stayed quietly by the tree. He listened and he watched.

Then something moved. It was only a little brown bird looking for bugs in the brush. Then there was another sound—a crashing sound. Something very big was coming. Was it a deer? No, it was too big for a deer. It must be a bear!

"Uncle," he shouted. "Where are you?" He shouted again. "Uncle!"

He began to run. The big animal ran too, and now he saw that it was a great stag. It bounded away into the forest.

Many-Deer was standing in the path. "You frightened the stag away!" he said. "Didn't I tell you to stand quietly? Why did you shout like that?"

"I thought it was a bear," said Chipmunk.

"A bear!" said his uncle. "I would not have let a bear come near you. You knew I was watching close by. You have much to learn if you are going to be a hunter."

They went on into the forest, but they saw no more deer that day. At last they went back to the village.

Next morning, Many-Deer and Chipmunk started out again.

"Now remember, no running and shouting today," said Many-Deer. He went first and Chipmunk followed.

"I mustn't be afraid. I mustn't be afraid," he said to himself.

He looked up at the great trees. He could not see the sky. He heard only the wind going "sh-sh-sh" in the treetops. Then something was over his head. It was a great bird. It moved through the trees without a sound.

Chipmunk was so frightened that he began to run. His feet cracked the branches and leaves on the ground and the bird was gone.

Many-Deer was standing still in the path when Chipmunk ran into him. He was very angry.

"Why do you do this?" Many-Deer asked. "I said that you were not to run."

"But that great big bird!" said Chipmunk. "It was flying over my head."

"That was an owl," said Many-Deer. "It was flying to its nest after a long night's hunting. You have frightened all the game in this part of the forest. Now we will have to go to another place. See if you can be like a hunter—not like a frightened rabbit."

"Yes, Uncle," said Chipmunk in a very small voice.

He followed his uncle along the trail. On and on they went, far into the forest. At last Chipmunk stopped to rest. But when he was ready to start again, he could not see his uncle. He looked for the trail, but he could not find it. There were trees on all sides, but he saw no knife marks on them.

He heard the sound of the brook, but the brook was far away, somewhere below him. He looked down and saw green leaves and green branches. The ground at his feet just dropped away. He was standing on the rim of a deep gorge. The gorge was so deep that he could look out over the tops of the trees that grew there. The brook was far down in the gorge.

He was alone in this strange still forest. He was lost!

"Uncle!" he shouted. "Where are you?"

He began to run. He pushed his way through the brush.

"I am here," said Many-Deer, "here in the path."

Why, his voice sounded very near! There was the trail, only a little way back from the gorge. Chipmunk waited there with his head down.

Many-Deer did not smile.

"You are not ready to be a hunter," he said. "Go back to the village."

ONCE A FOREST

There's a whirring sound in the forest,
"Timber!" the voices call.
I hear the buzz of a busy saw
And the crack of trees that fall.

And now where once was a forest,
Are houses row on row.
I wonder about that forest.
Where did the animals go?

Patricia Miles Martin

No, No, Rosina

Rosina's family had the most beautiful fishing boat in the fleet. And never once had she gone crab fishing with her father and her brothers and her uncle. NEVER once.

"Papa, can I go?" Rosina asked.

"You ask again!" Papa said. "The little one asks again."

"You're too young," Mama said.

"But when Luigi and Carlo are gone, I'm lonesome," Rosina said.

"Never mind," said Mama. "Next week you will all be back in school."

"But what about now?" Rosina asked.

"No, no, Rosina," said Luigi. "A fishing boat is no place for a little girl."

While she ate her breakfast, Rosina thought about the talk of the morning. This time when she asked to go, Papa had not said no. Not exactly.

Then Rosina knew what she would do. She would go aboard the Santa Rosa. She would hide on the Santa Rosa and surprise Papa.

Papa and the brothers were still eating.

Rosina ran along the sidewalk down to the dock.

There in the morning fog the Santa Rosa waited, rocking against the ladder that led down from the dock.

Rosina went down the ladder. She went aboard, and she looked for a place to hide.

On deck was a big crab box, ready for the day's catch. And there inside the little cabin was an old coat hanging on a peg—almost as if it were waiting for Rosina. She hid inside the coat and waited.

192

Everyone on land was starting to go to work.

People were calling to each other.

Then Papa and Rosina's brothers were coming down the ladder—and they were aboard. And Uncle came aboard too.

The Santa Rosa was leaving the dock—heading for the Golden Gate. And then it was chugging through the Golden Gate, and on to find the yellow floats that marked the place where their own crab pots lay deep in the water.

"Here are our crab pots," Papa shouted.

"Lots of crabs," Luigi said.

This was the time for Rosina. "Guess who's here," she said.

"It's Rosina," Luigi said. "It's Rosina, Papa."

Papa held his head. He was very angry.

"I will talk to you later about this," he said. "Carlo, radio ashore and say to tell Mama that we have Rosina." He looked at Luigi. "Why do we stand here? We have work to do."

Luigi put the crabs in the wooden box. "They look small," he said.

"They are TOO small," said Uncle. "Not one is big enough to keep."

Uncle threw the little crabs into the sea.
They chugged on to the next crab pot.

"Look," said Papa. "Not one is big enough
to keep."

The third crab pot was filled.

"These look better," said Uncle.

All morning they worked. Rosina helped.
They put big crabs into the big crab box
and dropped the little ones back into the
sea.

"We have had good luck today," said Rosina. Papa didn't answer.

Carlo spoke softly. "Look at the crabs, Papa. We have a good catch."

When the fog cleared and the sun was high, they started for the Golden Gate.

Rosina knew that she could never again ask Papa to go on the Santa Rosa. This was one day she would remember. She would remember every bit of it. She waved at all the other fishing boats. She waved at people on land. And when they reached the dock, she was the last to go up the ladder.

At home Papa talked with Rosina. He talked for a long time. And then he said, "Now you will talk with Mama."

"I'm sorry," Rosina said to Mama. "I'll never go away again without telling you first."

197

The next morning Rosina called to her brothers.

"Rise and shine," Rosina said. "Hit the deck. Up, Luigi. Up, Carlo."

Again Rosina would be at home alone.

"Cheer up," said Carlo. "Luigi and I have to work at the dock today. And today Mama and Papa are going to let you go——again!"

Rosina was too happy to talk. She had NEVER been so happy. She put on Luigi's yellow coat. She put on Carlo's hat.

Papa was shouting.

"Let's fix a good lunch," he said, as he patted the top of Carlo's hat. "We'll fix a good lunch for me and my crew."

Vacation

It was only the first day of vacation, but already something was going on in front of Suzu's house. Suzu rushed outside. Her neighbor, Mrs. Bell, was looking up into an oak tree near the walk.

"What's in the tree?" Suzu said.

"It's Mike. A pet monkey," Mrs. Bell said. "I told my brother I'd keep it until after vacation. And wouldn't you know, the monkey's loose already. Already!"

Mrs. Bell had a little sack in one hand. She took one peanut from the sack. "Come on, Mike—come on."

Mike came down, grabbed the peanut, and climbed into the tree again. He curled his tail around a high branch and sat there, eating the peanut.

Mr. Sing came by. "What's going on?" he asked.

"A pet monkey is loose in the tree," Suzu said.

200

"I wish I could help," Mr. Sing said. "But I can't stop to catch a monkey. I have to catch a bus. Why don't you call the zoo? If he belonged to me, I'd take him to the zoo and leave him there."

Jill Brown came running down the street. "Did I hear that there's a monkey loose in that tree?" she said. "Let ME get him down."

Up she went. But the monkey went higher. When she could almost reach him, the monkey swung up to the branch above.

"This could go on all day," Mrs. Bell said.

Jill came back down the tree.

Then Suzu thought of something. "Can I have a peanut?" she asked.

"Take the sack," Mrs. Bell said.

Suzu sat down under the tree. She ate a peanut. "Yum. Good," she said.

Mike swung down to a low branch. Suzu ate another peanut. The monkey swung to the lowest branch and dropped to the ground. He hopped up on her lap. He put one long arm around her neck and dipped one little paw into the sack.

"Here's your monkey, Mrs. Bell," Suzu said.

"Thank you, Suzu," Mrs. Bell said. "I'll CERTAINLY be glad when vacation's over."

What Is the Secret?

Read all the words and phrases in each group. Can you find how they are all alike?

1. boat   coat   moan

   road   goat   roam

   soap   croak   foam

2. outside   a pounding

   a bounce   a round cloud

   flour   a house mouse

   pouting   loud sounds

   shouts   found a hound

How would *you* group these?

   knick knack   gladness

   glass   a knife

   gliding   knocking

   knowing   a glow

Make a list of things that are alike in some way. See if the others can guess your secret.

Using phoneme-grapheme correspondences to decode and categorize words

Can You Solve a Puzzle?

Make this on your paper

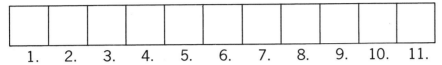

Write in each square on your paper only the first letter of the following words in the order given and you will have the name of someone in your family.

1. This is an animal with a long, long neck.

2. This is an animal with a mask on its face.

3. Carmelita went there.

4. You hear this when many children play.

5. Stanley is one.

6. A cow gives this.

7. A kind of tree that a bear climbed.

8. Five and five make this.

9. In the summer the weather is this.

10. This is an animal with a trunk.

11. Some people carry an umbrella when it does this.

Tales of
Couldn't Be

MICE

I think mice
Are rather nice.

Their tails are long,
Their faces small,
They haven't any
Chins at all.
Their ears are pink,
Their teeth are white,
They run about
The house at night.
They nibble things
They shouldn't touch
And no one seems
To like them much.

But I think mice
Are nice.

Rose Fyleman

208

THE MEETING OF THE MICE

CHARACTERS

OLD MOUSE	BIRD
MIDDLE HOUSE MOUSE	BIG FIELD MOUSE
SMALL MOUSE	MIDDLE FIELD MOUSE
VERY SMALL MICE	LITTLE FIELD MOUSE
CAT	TINY FIELD MICE

ACT ONE

COMMENTATOR: All the little house mice live
under the stairs in a big white
house. Outside the hole, which
is the door to their house, is
a fat cat, waiting—waiting—

*(The mice sit quietly under the stairs. Old Mouse
goes to the hole, looks through, and backs away.)*

SMALL MOUSE:	Did you see anything?
	Anything at all?
OLD MOUSE:	That cat is out there again.
	She is sitting out there waiting.
SMALL MOUSE:	What is she waiting for?
OLD MOUSE:	She is waiting for US.
MIDDLE HOUSE MOUSE:	She comes on soft feet. I wish
	I could hear her when she comes.
SMALL MOUSE:	I wish I could hear her when
	she goes away.
MIDDLE HOUSE MOUSE:	If she would ONLY bark like a
	dog, THEN we would hear her.
	We would know that SOMETHING
	was out there.
SMALL MOUSE:	If she would ONLY make a noise
	like a cat, we would know
	EXACTLY what was there.
VERY SMALL MICE:	(*Softly*) THEN we'd know!

OLD MOUSE: Something must be done.
Something—

MIDDLE HOUSE MOUSE: Is there anything we can do?

SMALL MOUSE: Anything at all?

OLD MOUSE: I don't know. But I'll call a
meeting of the mice, and we can
decide what to do.

ACT TWO

COMMENTATOR: Outside the mouse house
a bird flies here and there. It
flies near the mouse house,
chirping softly.

OLD MOUSE: (*From inside the house*)
BIRD, BIRD, CAN YOU HEAR ME?

BIRD: (*Chirping*) I hear you, I hear you,
Old Mouse.

OLD MOUSE: Will you do something for us?

BIRD: (*Chirping*) I'll do anything I can—
anything I can—

OLD MOUSE: Will you please call a meeting
of the mice? Will you ask them to
meet us here tonight?

BIRD: (*Chirping*) Yes, I will—yes, I will—

COMMENTATOR: The bird flies away, and at
last it flies over a corn field
where little field mice
are eating corn.

BIRD: (*Bird is chirping as it flies
down, and the field mice stop
to listen.*)
I am calling the mice
to a meeting—to a meeting—
tonight—tonight—tonight.

BIG FIELD MOUSE: And where is the meeting to be,
Bird ?

BIRD: (*Chirping*) Under the stairs—
under the stairs—in the big house—
big house. (*It flies away.*)

ACT THREE

COMMENTATOR: Night comes and the cat
lies down to sleep.

CAT: (*Cat goes to her bed and lies
down to sleep.*) Purr—purr—purr—

(*The field mice creep into the big house and through
the hole, into the mouse house. The mice sit together
in a ring.*)

OLD MOUSE: There is a fat cat that sits
outside our door every day.

MIDDLE FIELD MOUSE: WE know.

TINY LITTLE FIELD MICE: (*Softly*) We know—

LITTLE FIELD MOUSE: We know because that cat
prowls in OUR field of corn.

BIG FIELD MOUSE: SOMETHING has to be done
about that cat.

214

OLD MOUSE: That is exactly why I have called this meeting. We must decide what to do.

BIG FIELD MOUSE: I know exactly what to do. We must get a bell. If we have a bell, we can put it on the cat's neck. Any old bell will do. Any bell at all.

ALL MICE: HEAR—HEAR—

BIG FIELD MOUSE: It will be easy—VERY easy to find a bell somewhere in this big house.

ACT FOUR

COMMENTATOR: The mice look for the bell.

(Mice creep out through the hole.)

MIDDLE HOUSE MOUSE: There should be SOMETHING here in the kitchen.

LITTLE FIELD MOUSE: There is nothing here.

MIDDLE FIELD MOUSE: Not even a bit of corn.

MIDDLE HOUSE MOUSE: Not even a bite of cake.

LITTLE FIELD MOUSE: Not even any little seeds.

SMALL MOUSE: Not even a bit of bun.

BIG FIELD MOUSE: The bell ! The bell ! Let us not forget what we are looking for !

COMMENTATOR: The mice creep quietly up the stairs.

216

CAT:	Purr—purr—
BIG FIELD MOUSE:	What's THAT I hear?
OLD HOUSE MOUSE:	It's the cat.
MIDDLE HOUSE MOUSE:	When we hear her purr, we know we're safe.
SMALL MOUSE:	Because she's asleep in her bed.
MIDDLE HOUSE MOUSE:	Maybe there is something in these boxes.

(The mice hunt through the boxes.)

SMALL MOUSE:	And there IS something! See what I have found. Listen. *(He jingles a very little bell. Jingle jingle.)*
VERY SMALL MICE, *and* TINY FIELD MICE:	*(Softly)* A LITTLE bell!
BIG FIELD MOUSE:	That's a bell for a cat. It's exactly what we want.

COMMENTATOR: The mice go back down the stairs.

CAT: Purr—purr—purr—

BIG FIELD MOUSE: Hurry—hurry—

(The mice go through the hole and into the mouse house. They sit together in a ring.)

SMALL MOUSE: *(Jingles bell softly.)*
I have been thinking of something.

BIG FIELD MOUSE: This is a great thing!

MIDDLE FIELD MOUSE: Yes! We have a bell for that cat.

SMALL MOUSE: May I say something?
(He jingles the bell softly.)

BIG FIELD MOUSE: And I am the mouse who thought of finding the bell!

ALL MICE: HEAR—HEAR—

SMALL MOUSE: Please, may I ask something?

OLD MOUSE: Ask anything you wish—

SMALL MOUSE:	Who will put the bell on the cat?
ALL MICE:	Not I!
	Not I!
	I won't!
	I won't!
SMALL MOUSE:	It makes ME afraid even to think about it.
OLD MOUSE:	Then we can do nothing.
SMALL MOUSE:	(*He softly jingles the bell.*) It is easy to decide what to do— But to do it—well, THAT'S not easy—not easy at all!
COMMENTATOR:	All the mice nod, and because it is almost morning, the field mice hurry back to their field of corn, and the little house mice sit very still and listen for the cat.

THE GOBLIN

A goblin lives in our house, in our house, in
   our house,
A goblin lives in our house all the year
   round.
He bumps
And he jumps
And he thumps
And he stumps.
He knocks
And he rocks
And he rattles at the locks.
A goblin lives in our house, in our house, in
   our house,
A goblin lives in our house all the year
   round.

Rose Fyleman

Here We Go

Once there was a farmer and wife who had a fine farm, some fine horses and cows, a fine big house, and six fine children. They were a happy family—happy, that is, but for one thing. There was a boggart in the house.

Boggart is the north-of-England name for a trick-playing spirit which moves into people's houses and barns and plays jokes on everyone.

This house had a boggart. The boggart would often walk around the house at night and take the sheets off of people. Sometimes it rapped on the door, but when someone got up, there would be no one there.

Often it would fall downstairs in the dark and make a great noise, and when the farmer or the wife ran into the bedroom—afraid it was one of the children—all the children would be asleep in bed.

Sometimes it would just tap, tap, tap in the night. Sometimes it rolled a ball across the floor time and again, so no one could sleep. One night it threw all the pots and pans down the stairs.

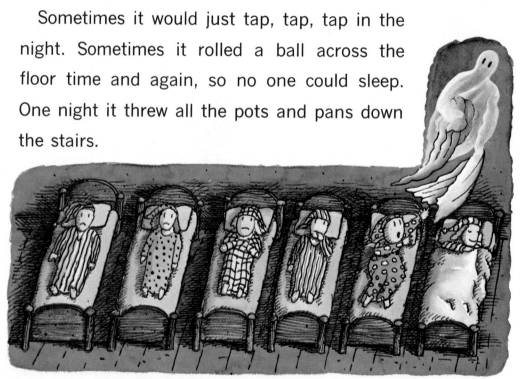

Once in a while the boggart would help the family. It would wash the dishes when no one was looking. It would feed and water the horses and cows. But more often than not it would let them out, so someone had to go looking for them.

One of the things it liked to do was to blow the smoke back DOWN the chimney whenever anyone started to light a fire. Or it would blow out the flame just when someone wanted to make a light.

At last the family had enough of all this. Something had to be done.

So they decided to move. They decided to move to a new house on a big farm far away where there would be no boggarts.

The family packed up all their things and piled them high on the big wagon.

As they were about to drive off, a neighbor came by and said, "Oh, are you moving?"

"Yes," said the farmer. And he told the neighbor that they could not stand their boggart any longer, so they were moving.

So the neighbor wished them luck, and they drove off.

Then from the top of the load they heard a happy little voice say, "Well, here we go! We're off!"

THE MOUSE WHO
LIKED TO READ IN BED

Scuffie was a little field mouse who liked to
read in bed.

On a little night stand beside his bed was
a pink birthday candle. The candle was his
reading light.

Scuffie often chewed bits of paper and made
them look like books.

One night his mother came in when he had just gone to bed and was ready to read.

"Scuffie," she said. "I don't think it is good for you to read so much in bed. And look at your candle. It has dripped down on your bed."

"Please let me read for a little while. I have all these books to read."

"All right," said his mother, "but don't read a long book. And don't forget to shut your outside door. You know why, don't you?"

"Yes, Mother, I know why," Scuffie said.

"You really should shut it right now," his mother said. And she gave him a small good-night mouse kiss.

When she was gone, Scuffie thought, "I really should get up and shut the door right now. I will do it in a little while."

He started to read. Then he heard something outside.

"What is that?" he thought.

It was his neighbors, Big Beetle and Little Beetle, who lived nearby.

"Hello," said Big Beetle. "I see that you are reading in bed."

"And with your door wide open," said Little Beetle. "You really should NOT do that, you know."

The beetles crawled away.

"I really should get up and shut the door right now," said Scuffie. "I will do it in a little while."

He started to read.

Then he heard a sound like a tail hitting the ground—thump—thump—thump—

He heard it again—thump—thump—

He looked up.

There was the cat.

"Oh my," Scuffie thought. "I should never have left my door open. It's too late to shut it now—"

"I see you," said the cat. "You are reading in bed."

Now Scuffie was very frightened. There was the cat, so big—so big—and there he was, just a little, little mouse—

But he said in a brave little voice, "Would you like to hear me read a story? I will read a story to you if you would like to listen."

The cat looked at Scuffie. "I'll listen if you read a good cat story."

Scuffie began to make up a story.

His voice was high and frightened.

He read, "The people in this neighborhood are having a BIG day tomorrow. Tomorrow is going to be Cat Chasing Day. They will get umbrellas and sticks and run after cats. So all cats should go somewhere else right away, and stay away all day tomorrow. For tomorrow, Cat Chasing Day, will be a bad day for cats—"

Scuffie waited for the cat to say something, but the cat didn't say anything at all.

When Scuffie looked at the doorway, he had a great surprise. The cat had gone.

Scuffie got up and shut the door.

He had just popped into bed again when his mother and father came in.

"Scuffie," his mother said. "If you MUST read a story in bed, please read softly. You make too much noise."

"And now it is really time to put out your light," said his father.

As they left Scuffie heard his mother say, "I am glad he remembered to shut his door."

"I'll remember tomorrow," Scuffie said to himself. "I'll remember to shut it tomorrow and every night after this." He put out his candle and lay in his bed shivering.

Then he was very hungry. He remembered the pink candle that had dripped on his bed.

After he ate that off, he wasn't afraid any more, and he stopped shivering and fell asleep.

The Raccoon and Mrs. McGinnis

A little raccoon who was almost tame
lived in an old apple tree. He had a black mask
on his face and six black rings on his tail.

There, in the woods by the old apple tree,
was a little house where Mrs. McGinnis lived.

232

Mrs. McGinnis had one cow and two pigs.
She took armloads of hay to the cow
and pails of corn to the pigs.

And every night the cow and the pigs
went to sleep under the apple tree.

Then she put a slice of bread on the doorstep
for the raccoon, and the raccoon knew
that the bread was for him.

One night she was standing
in front of her house, as she often did.
She looked up and saw a star.

"That's the first star I have seen tonight,
indeed it is," she said. "I will make a wish.
Indeed I will." She looked up at the star.
"I wish for a little barn, so my cow and my pigs
will be safe from the wind and the rain."
Then she put a slice of bread on her step.

233

After Mrs. McGinnis had gone to bed,
the raccoon came down from the tree
and picked up the bread.

He walked into the woods until he came
to a river. Beside the river he swished
the bread in the water, because
that is what a raccoon often does.
When the bread was wet, he ate it.

Because he was still hungry, he started to look
for something more to eat. Just as he started
to look, he heard something coming down the road.
Two men came along on their horses. The raccoon
hid in back of a tree.

234

The men got down from their horses.

"Mrs. McGinnis is not far from here,"
the first man said. "We will leave our horses here,
and we will go to Mrs. McGinnis's house.
We will go very quietly, and we will take
her cow and pigs. She will not know they are gone
until morning."

The men put black masks over their faces
and started down the road. The raccoon followed.
The men made no noise. When they reached
the apple tree, they took the cow and the pigs
and started back through the woods.
The little raccoon still followed.

He followed quietly. Then he stepped on
a small branch, and the branch broke with a CRACK.

"What was that?" asked the first man.

"It was nothing," said the other.

"Little night animals often play here."

Then a small rock rolled down the hill
and into the river. It made a splash.

"What was that?" asked the first man.

"It was nothing," said the other. "Nothing at all."
Often little fish jump and splash in the water.

Everything was very still until a rabbit
ran down the road.

"I think someone is following us,"
the first man said.

The little raccoon thought he would climb
a tree because there he would be safe from danger.
He climbed up and looked around the tree
to see where the men were.

In the moonlight, only the black mask
of the little raccoon could be seen.

THE MEN WERE LOOKING RIGHT AT HIM.

"It is another masked bandit,"
said the first man.

"Don't shoot." said the other.
"You may take our cow and our pigs."

"Take our money too," said the first man.
"ONLY PLEASE DON'T SHOOT."

And as he ran to his horse,
he tossed a fat moneybag to the ground.
The men went off down the road
as fast as their horses could go.

The raccoon climbed down and
picked up the moneybag. He took it to the river
and swished it in the water.

The cow and the pigs started down the road
that led to the little house,
and the raccoon followed with the moneybag.

Because he often looked on the step for bread,
he went there to look. There was nothing on the step,
so he dropped the moneybag and went up the tree
to his bed.

In the morning Mrs. McGinnis came outside.

"What is this? It is a moneybag! Indeed it is! My wish has come true! Indeed it has! NOW I can have a barn for my cow and my pigs."

Builders came, and soon there was a barn where no barn had been before.

At night, Mrs. McGinnis would often lean against the apple tree, look up at the stars, and say, "My cow and my pigs are safe in the barn, and ALL because I wished upon a star." That is what she thought !

Then she would put something on her step.

And after a while the little raccoon, who was almost tame, would climb down from the tree. Then he would look on the step because he knew that she had put a slice of bread there, just for him.

241

The Partridge and the Fox

A hungry old fox was hunting for his supper. He saw a fat partridge in the brush. He did not want to frighten her away, so he sat down and spoke softly. "What a beautiful bird you are! Your feathers are purple in the sun. I have never seen a bird so beautiful."

The partridge preened her feathers.

"How beautiful!" the fox said. "I wish I could see you when you sleep. I imagine you are even more beautiful when you are sleeping."

The partridge shut her eyes.

POUNCE.

The fox had her in his jaws.

"OH!" the partridge said. "Fox, PLEASE tell me one more time how beautiful I am. Tell me once more that my feathers are purple in the sun. Then kill me for your supper."

The fox spoke. "You are. . . ." The partridge was gone—high into an apple tree.

The fox looked up at her. "Now WHY did I open my mouth?" he said.

"WHY did I shut my eyes?" said the partridge.

And the hungry old fox went on his way through the brush, looking for his supper.

Old Tales

Some stories have been read by many people for a long, long time. Fables are one kind of old story. Some fables are as much as 2000 years old. Some may be older.

All fables are short. In most fables, instead of people talking, animals or objects speak. Most of the time in a fable only one important thing happens, and from what happens a lesson can be learned.

You know some fables. "The Hare and the Tortoise," and "The Ant and the Grasshopper" are the names of two that you may remember.

Here is a picture of a fable. If you don't know the story, can you make up one?

Old and New Ways of Saying Things

When things have been said the same way many times they lose their freshness. Stale sayings are called clichés. Can you think of some? Tell the missing word in these clichés.

1.

High as a house

Quiet as a _____

2.

Bold as brass

Clear as _____

3.

White as a sheet

Red as a _____

4.

Blue as the sky

Nice as _____

Now think of a new fresh way to say an old phrase. Instead of saying "cool as a cucumber" you could say "cool as an ice cube on a hot summer day." Try saying these in your own way.

Black as coal

White as a ghost

Warm as toast

Light as a feather

Fox and the Fire

Fox and the Fire

The young red fox stood near a cave on the side of a mountain.

For three days, a strange smell of danger had come with the wind. Now with the smell of danger, came the good smell of rabbit.

And the young red fox was hungry.

She started out to catch her supper.

She made no noise.

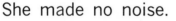

248

Close by, a gentle rabbit nibbled a weed.

The fox saw it and crept close.

Before the fox could catch her supper, a blue jay came low and screeched in anger, and the rabbit flashed into its burrow.

The fox whimpered, and sniffed at the burrow and scratched at the earth.

And even as she whimpered, gray-black smoke came heavy with the wind. Far away, in the forest, fire crawled along the ground and dry leaves snapped and crackled in its path.

The fox heard the roar of fire leaping from one tree to another, and she knew she must run.

At first she was bewildered and did not know which way to go.

Rabbits and mice came from their hiding places. Squirrels darted along the ground and quail called from the greasewood.

Two squirrels ran by and the fox followed behind them.

Sparrows and blue jays flew low overhead as the crackle of fire came closer.

Together, the animals ran out of the forest and the fox forgot that she was hungry.

On they went, across green fields until they came to a road.

The fox followed beside the road.

She came to a low brown house with a big tree growing beside it.

Beyond the tree was a barn.

Between the barn and the house was a pen, and inside the pen, a small chicken house.

With the strong, close smell of chicken came the smell of human and dog.

The fox shivered, ready to run, but there was no place to go.

Inside the house, a dog barked wildly, and the fox ran to the barn. Under the barn she found a small hole where she could hide.

She lay there——her nose on her paws—— watching——

Rabbits and chipmunks, squirrels and mice, found hiding places. Squirrels and chipmunks went up in the tree, and rabbits and mice under the house.

Five deer came, and lay down close beside the barn.

The fox felt the shake of the earth when the fire trucks rolled up, their red lights flashing and their sirens screeching.

Cars came with people to help fight the fire. With shovels and spades, they turned the earth. Tanker trucks came and a fire fighting bomber flew low overhead.

Inside the house, the dog howled like a wild animal.

In the hours that followed, the fox huddled small in her hiding place.

The people at the ranch fought the fire with the fire fighters, and the fire was held back. The house, the barn, and the tree were saved.

When the fire was out, all the people went inside the house, and the fox remembered that she was hungry.

She crept from under the barn and went up to the house.

Through a window she saw a big black dog, walking back and forth.

The fox crept toward the road. When the earth was cool, she trotted back over the black fields.

The fox found her cave on the side of the mountain, but the leaves and grass were burned and the mountain was bare.

She hunted for her breakfast, but the rabbits and the mice had gone to new hiding places and the fox found nothing.

She hunted all day, and when night came, she started out across the black fields.

When she reached the ranch, she stopped. There was no sound from the low brown house.

The fox crept toward the chicken house.

With a mighty leap, the thin, hungry fox was over the fence.

Without making a sound, she went into the chicken house.

255

She reached up and seized a chicken. With one quick shake of her head, it was dead.

The chickens set up a great squawking, and the fox leaped up and over the fence and away.

The door to the house opened. People shouted and a dog barked. Then the dog came leaping through the doorway.

The fox ran toward the road.

She galloped along beside the fence.

The bark of the dog was close—closer—

The fox leaped to the top rail of the fence and waited there in the dark.

The dog did not see her,
and went racing by.

The fox went on along the top of the fence.
Far away, she could hear the bark of the dog.

Back in the barnyard, the dog trotted
around the chicken pen, and chickens scolded
softly and settled down again to sleep.

The fox did not return.

257

In the days that followed, seeds were planted in the burned earth, and clover and wild grass grew again.

In the forest, new branches grew green, and little animals found shelter in trees and in burrows.

258

The fox hunted for her supper.

And when she had eaten, she lay safe in her cave, and she cleaned her fur and pulled the burrs from between her toes.

When the moon rose low over the valley, she went outside and rolled in the dirt and shook herself.

She pointed her nose toward the moon and howled.

From far away, she heard a bark—a warning bark.

Far down in the valley, the black dog was answering her call.

The fox sniffed the air, and she smelled the good, cool, damp smell of green growing things, and trotted off into the forest.

New Words in This Book

The following new words are presented in *The Dog Next Door and Other Stories,* Level 7, Reading 720. Words listed with underscores are new enrichment words. Those words listed without underscores are new basic words. Because of the large number of decodable words in this book, they are not listed here. Decodable words for each selection are listed in the Teacher's Edition.

	UNIT 1							
Page		19	decided	38	floor	54	refrigerator
8	Bradleys		opened		once		snack
	door		proudly	39	flip	55	beautiful
	move	22	drop		only		hogan
	William	23	own	40	against	56	cactus
	doorway	24	listened		exactly		quail
9	family		hurried		held		quietly
	movers		swish	41	any	57	rattle
	moving	26	hair	43	puppy	58	language
10	front		hurry		**UNIT 2**	60	corn
	Stanley	27	ahead	48	Jonathan		pail
12	climbed		barber		paint		field
	higher		bicycle	49	parade		thirsty
	oak		push		stomach	61	high
13	almost	28	window		beetles		stories
	does	29	chair		curled	62	coyote
15	better	31	gone		hurried	63	camp
	gardens	32	telephone		turned		coffee
	having		until	50	ground		chipmunks
17	rain		worried		head	64	can opener
	umbrella	34	across		robin		valleys
18	through		showed		worm	65	borrow
		36	crawled	53	I've		Lisa

262

66	campfire	102	flat	139	found		because
67	snake		lies		litter		doughnuts
	slid		flashing	140	department	158	skate
69	dinner	*heard* 103	herd	141	always	159	Johnny
	slowly	105	beavers	142	rattles		Trudy
72	afraid		drink	144	click		
	skunk	106	chew	145	bulbs		**UNIT 5**
	Daddy		young		Henry	168	Augustus
75	love	107	danger		tulips		Gloriana
77	branch	109	above	146	multiplied		Jupiter
	crow	112	armloads	147	glad		river
	neighborhood		tunnels		knocked		chickens
78	left	113	low	148	grew		Mississippi
	shirt	115	otter	149	neighbors	169	tossed
	spool	116	floats	152	built	170	drifting
	thread	119	clam		Washington, D.C.	173	cabin
79	low	122	pulls		rivers		hound
82	sorry			153	capitol		shivering
					president		crossed
			UNIT 4		United States	174	flood
	UNIT 3	130	Carmelita	155	cherry	177	middle
88	forest		Ricardo		elevator		Chippewa
	supper	131	aquarium		George		Indian
89	bear		Grandma		highest	178	breakfast
	crash	132	great		monuments		enough
90	hungry		idea	156	Arlington Cemetery		uncle
91	broke	133	voice		capital		village
93	brush		forth		died		sons
94	enemies	135	really	157	Clover	179	knife
96	prowls	136	candles		trio		arrows
98	pronghorn	138	torn		apples		lucky

263

180	bring		radio		field	225	Scuffie
	brook		wooden		tiny	226	dripped
	brave	195	threw		characters	227	really
	kept		third	211	done		should
181	bubbling	196	cleared	212	chirping		good-night
183	shouted		spoke		flies	228	thump
	bounded	198	crew	215	easy	230	read (past)
184	frightened	199	already	216	even		tomorrow
186	angry		monkey		kitchen	232	apple
187	gorge		vacation		nothing		mask
190	Luigi		neighbor		should		McGinnis
	Mama	200	curled	217	jingles	233	bread
	never	201	swung	221	boggart	234	because
	Papa	202	lowest		England	236	nothing
	Rosina	203	certainly		spirit	240	builders
191	aboard			223	chimney		true
	Santa Rosa			224	drive	242	feathers
192	ladder		**UNIT 6**		drove		partridge
194	golden	209	act		wagon	243	preened
	ashore		commentator				

Illustrations and photographs were provided by the following: Marc Brown (177–179, 181, 183–188); Richard Brown (221–224, 242–245); Ron Church—Photography Unlimited (115, 119); Tom Cooke (8–44); Leo and Diane Dillon (128–129, 137–140, 143–149); Len Ebert (130–136); Ed Emberley (232–241); Jeff Foott—Bruce Coleman, Inc. (116, 118, 120–123); Harold M. Lambert Studios, Inc. (150); Ted Lewin (48–54, 63–76); Frank Lucas (150); David M. McPhail (88–114, 152–156); Les Morrill (84); Jane Teiko Oka (220); Bob Owens (164); Arthur and Pauline Perry (208–219, 225–231); Ted Rand (190–193, 195–197, 199–203); H. Armstrong Roberts (150); John Schoenherr (247–261); Joel Snyder (55–62, 157–163); Arvis Stewart (77–83, 85); Earl Thollander (168–173, 175–176, 189); Stan Wayman—Photo Researchers, Inc. (117)

The cover and unit introduction pages were designed by Gregory Fossella Associates.

ABCDEFGHIJ 08543210
PRINTED IN THE UNITED STATES OF AMERICA